Carol Vorder

Maths Made Easy ExtraTests

Author and consultant Sean McArdle

Key Stage 1

AGES 5-6

LONDON, NEW YORK, MUNICH, MELBOURNE, and DELHI

DK UK
Senior Editor Deborah Lock
Art Director Martin Wilson
Publishing Director Sophie Mitchell
Pre-production Francesca Wardell
Jacket Designer Martin Wilson
Maths Consultant Sean McArdle

DK Delhi
Editorial Monica Saigal, Tanya Desai
Design Pallavi Narain, Dheeraj Arora,
Tanvi Nathyal, Jyotsna Khosla
DTP Designer Anita Yadav

First published in Great Britain by
Dorling Kindersley Limited
80 Strand, London, WC2R 0RL

Copyright © 2013 Dorling Kindersley Limited
A Penguin Company

10 9 8 7 6 5 4 3 2 1
001—187382—July/2013

A CIP catalogue record for this book
is available from the British Library

ISBN: 978-1-4093-6591-4

Printed and bound in China by L Rex Printing Co., Ltd.

All images © Dorling Kindersley
For further information see: www.dkimages.com

Discover more at
www.dk.com

Contents

This chart lists all the topics in the book. Once you have completed each page, stick a star in the correct box below.

Page	Topic	Star
4	Read, write, and draw	⭐
5	Tens and units	☆
6	Counting	☆
7	More or less	☆
8	Missing numbers	☆
9	Counting in 2s	☆
10	Counting in 10s	☆
11	Ordering	☆

Write each number as a word.

4 four	8	10	3
7	1	5	9
2	6	0	

Write each amount as a number and a word.

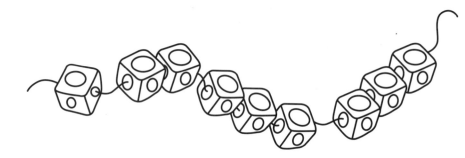

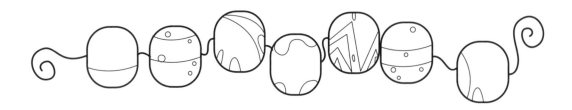

Draw the correct number of things.

Four   Two   Five 🌙   Three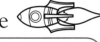

   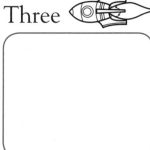

How many in each box?

Tens	Units
1	3

13

Tens	Units

Tens	Units

Draw each number as tens and units.

Tens	Units
1	2

12

Tens	Units

29

Tens	Units

36

Count in 3s, 4s, 5s, and 6s.

Complete each set.

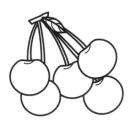 

5 is one more than

3 is one more than ☐

6 is one more than ☐

4 is one more than ☐

9 is one less than 10

☐ is one less than 15

☐ is one less than 16

☐ is one less than 13

Fill in the missing numbers on these carriages.

Draw the hops and count.

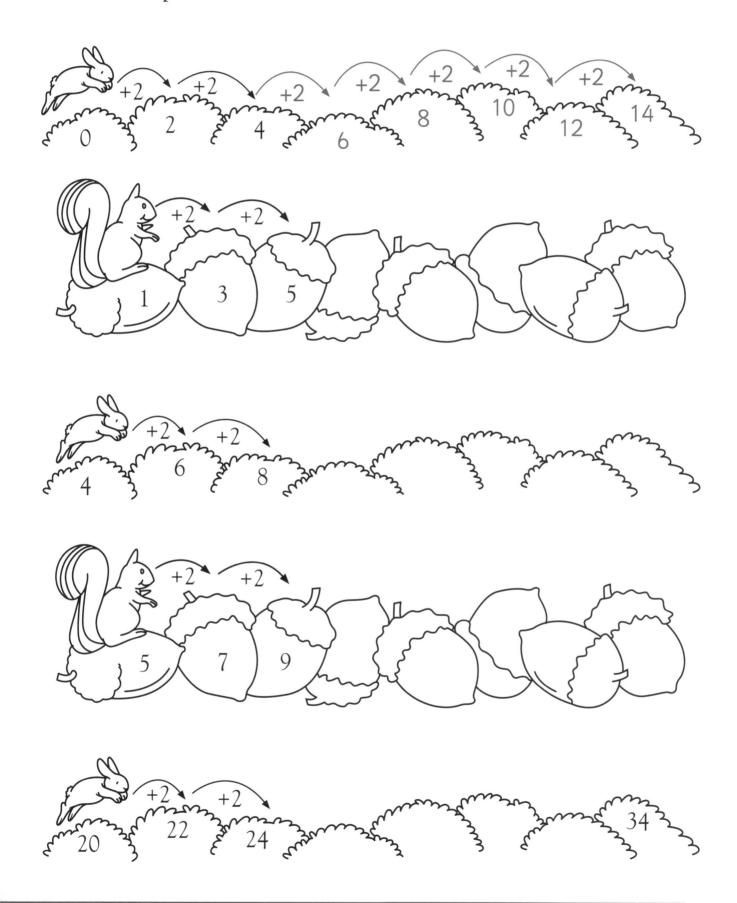

Counting in 10s

Fill in the missing numbers.

Write the numbers in each cloud in order with the largest number first.

10 7 9 2 0 3 → [10] [ ] [ ] [ ] [ ] [ ]

22 0 20 12 21 2 → [ ] [ ] [ ] [ ] [ ] [ ]

20 50 0 10 40 30 → [ ] [ ] [ ] [ ] [ ] [ ]

Write the numbers in each cloud in order with the smallest number first.

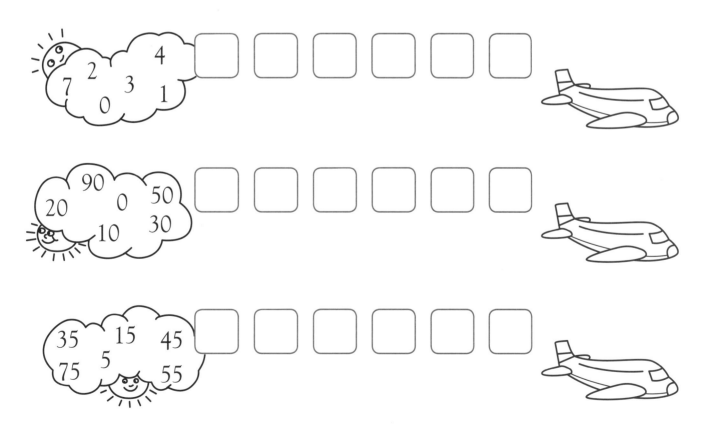

2 4 7 3 1 0 → [ ] [ ] [ ] [ ] [ ] [ ]

90 50 20 0 10 30 → [ ] [ ] [ ] [ ] [ ] [ ]

35 15 45 75 5 55 → [ ] [ ] [ ] [ ] [ ] [ ]

Fractions of shapes

Colour half ($\frac{1}{2}$) of each shape.

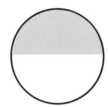 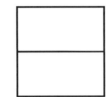 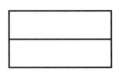

Now colour half ($\frac{1}{2}$) of each shape in a different way.

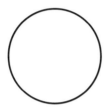  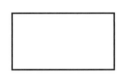

Colour a quarter ($\frac{1}{4}$) of each shape.

 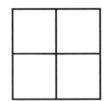 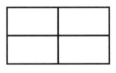

Now colour a quarter ($\frac{1}{4}$) of each shape in a different way.

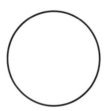  

What fraction of each shape is shaded?

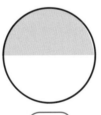 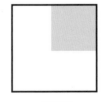 

Circle the number that is odd.

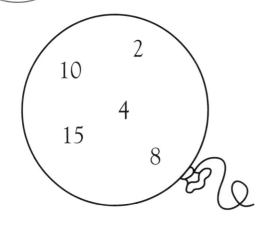

10 2
4
15
8

Circle the number that is **not** odd.

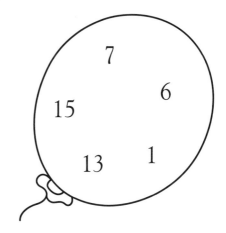

7
15 6
13 1

Circle the number that is even.

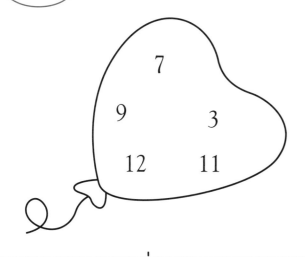

7
9 3
12 11

Circle the number that is **not** even.

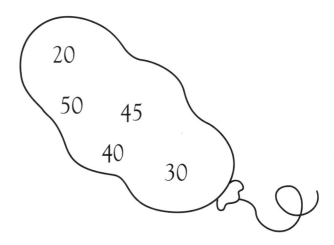

20
50 45
40
30

Write the next three odd numbers.

21   23   25   ☐ ☐ ☐

5   7   9   ☐ ☐ ☐

Write the next three even numbers.

24   26   28   ☐ ☐ ☐

66   68   70   ☐ ☐ ☐

Max needs 8 carrots. Cross out 8 carrots.

How many carrots are left? ☐

Ann has 15 cupcakes and buys 10 more.
How many cupcakes does Ann have altogether? ☐

Doors on one side of the road have odd numbers.
Fill in the missing numbers.

3   5   11

What is next in this sequence?

....

How many tens are there in each number?

14 ☐   36 ☐   51 ☐   20 ☐   75 ☐

Keeping skills sharp

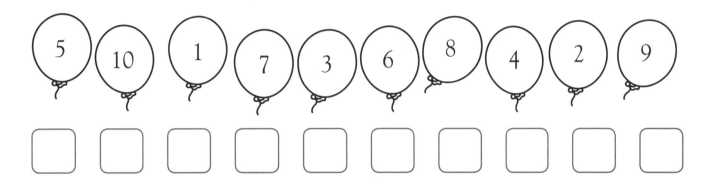

The race!

Smithy   Bonnie   Dan   Sanji

Who is 1st? ....   Who is 3rd? ....

Who is 2nd? ....   Who is 4th? ....

Write the numbers in order with the smallest number first.

5   10   1   7   3   6   8   4   2   9

☐ ☐ ☐ ☐ ☐ ☐ ☐ ☐ ☐ ☐

Write the amounts in order with the largest first.

2 p   1 p   5 p   10 p   20 p   50 p

☐ ☐ ☐ ☐ ☐ ☐

Each group has three chicks. How many chicks are there in three groups? ☐

How many are there in each row?

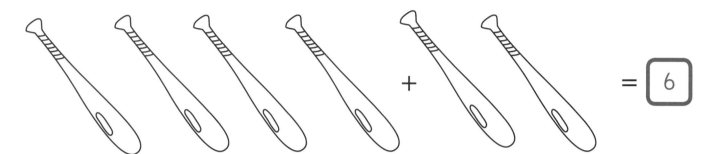

+ = 6

◯ ◯ ◯ ◯ + ◯ ◯ ◯ = ☐

+ = ☐

+ = ☐

Complete each sum.

3 + 1 = ☐   5 + 4 = ☐   7 + 3 = ☐

8 + 0 = ☐   9 + 2 = ☐   10 + 4 = ☐

4 + 8 = ☐   6 + 9 = ☐   13 + 6 = ☐

10 + 10 = ☐   17 + 2 = ☐   4 + 13 = ☐

How many more will make 10?

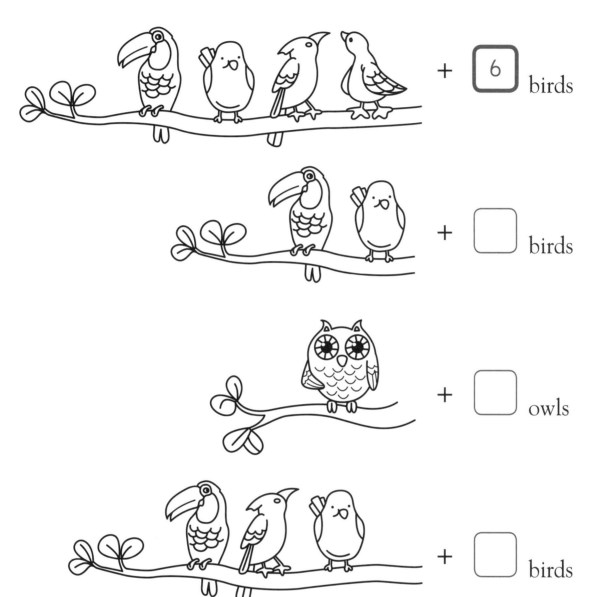

+ [6] birds

+ [   ] birds

+ [   ] owls

+ [   ] birds

Which number is missing?

3 + [   ] = 10

9 + [   ] = 10

[   ] + 5 = 10

[   ] + 6 = 10

4 + [   ] + 5 = 10

[   ] + 3 + 3 = 10

8 + 0 + [   ] = 10

1 + 2 + [   ] = 10

Reduce each amount by 3. **Hint**: Cross out 3 and count how many are left.

 1

Make each amount smaller by 2. **Hint**: Cross out 2 to help you.

      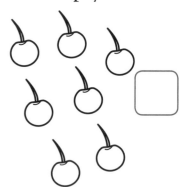

Lessen each amount by 4. **Hint**: Cross out 4 to help you.

   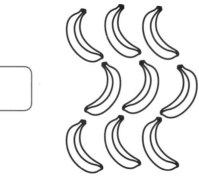   

Work out each sum.

$10 - 5 =$ ⬚ $9 - 6 =$ ⬚ $12 - 3 =$ ⬚

$14 - 10 =$ ⬚ $12 - 12 =$ ⬚ $10 - 8 =$ ⬚

How many are left?

Take 2 dots away from each cap.

7

Take 3 candles away from each cake.

Take 4 balloons away from each bunch.

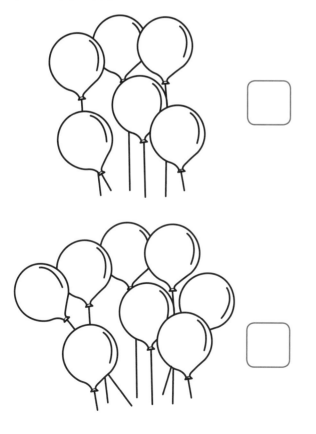

Take 5 presents away from each set.

What is double each number?

2 [4]   3 [   ]   4 [   ]   5 [   ]

1 [   ]   6 [   ]   7 [   ]   8 [   ]

Double each amount.

5 p [   ]   2 p [   ]   10 p [   ]   20 p [   ]

1 p [   ]   4 p [   ]   6 p [   ]   11 p [   ]

What were these numbers before they were doubled?

12 [   ]   10 [   ]   8 [   ]   6 [   ]

10 p [   ]   20 p [   ]   12 p [   ]   14 p [   ]

Try and double these larger numbers.

30 [   ]   40 [   ]   50 [   ]   100 [   ]

15 p [   ]   25 p [   ]   60 p [   ]   £6.00 [   ]

Counting in groups

Count in groups and write how many there are.

🐜🐜 + 🐜🐜 + 🐜🐜 + 🐜🐜 = **8**

🦋🦋🦋🦋 + 🦋🦋🦋🦋 + 🦋🦋🦋🦋 = ☐

🐞🐞🐞 + 🐞🐞🐞 = ☐

🐛🐛🐛🐛🐛 + 🐛🐛🐛🐛🐛 = ☐

Now solve these to find each total.

2 groups of 4 = ☐   3 groups of 5 = ☐

4 groups of 3 = ☐   7 groups of 2 = ☐

Molly is going on holiday and can only pack half of her T-shirts.
Cross out half of the T-shirts.

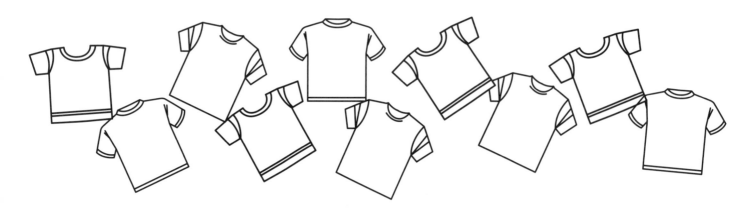

Fatima and Nima put their pet mice together.

Fatima has 8 mice and Nima has 6 mice.
How many mice do they have altogether?

Write the answers.

$3 + 4 =$ ⬚ $6 + 2 =$ ⬚ $5 + 5 =$ ⬚ $9 + 3 =$ ⬚

$10 - 2 =$ ⬚ $8 - 7 =$ ⬚ $5 - 4 =$ ⬚ $3 - 3 =$ ⬚

Fill in the box with the right symbol: <, >, or = .

32 ☐ 12   15 ☐ 15   17 ☐ 21

Clara has a bag with 9 sweets.   Olly has a bag with 6 sweets.

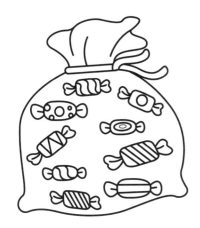   

How many more sweets does Clara have than Olly? ☐

Count how many there are.

⊛ ⊛ + ⊛ ⊛ + ⊛ ⊛ = ☐

🍭 🍭 🍭 + 🍭 🍭 🍭 = ☐

🍭🍭🍭 + 🍭🍭🍭 + 🍭🍭🍭 + 🍭🍭🍭 = ☐

Comparing money

What is the value of each coin?

     1 p

Draw the coins that make the same amount.

      =

           =

    =

     =

   =

 =

How much change will I get back?

 I pay   my change = 8 p

 I pay   my change =

 I pay  my change =

 I pay  my change =

 I pay  my change =

Circle the largest animal in each group.

Circle the smallest animal in each group.

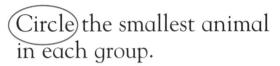

Circle the animal that is the tallest.

Circle the caterpillar that is the longest.

What time is it?

3 o'clock

Draw the time on each clock.

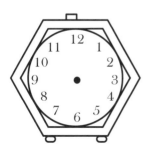

3 o'clock

7 o'clock

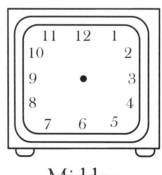

Midday

Which equations are true and which are false?
Mark each of them with a T for True or an F for False.

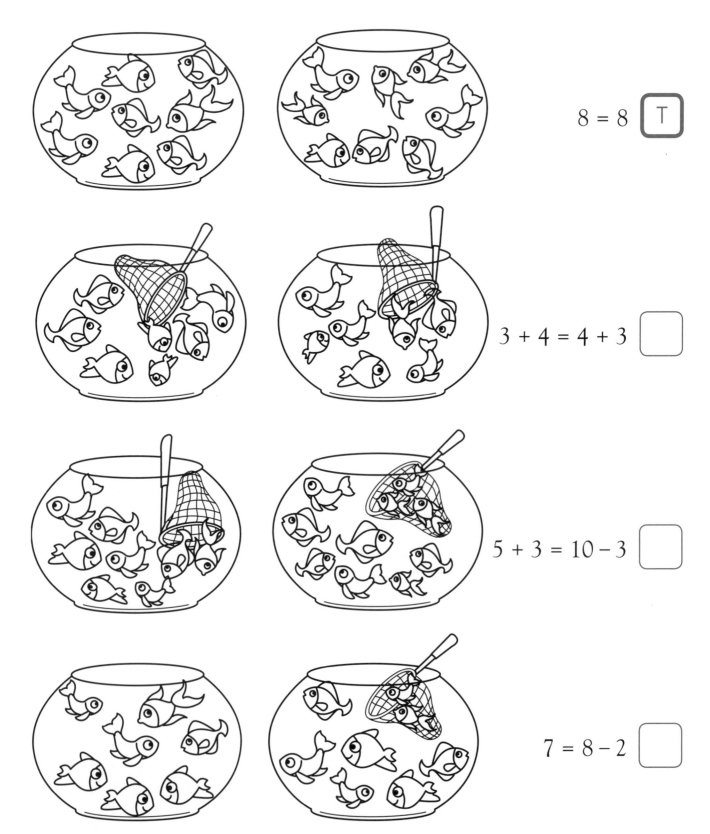

$8 = 8$ T

$3 + 4 = 4 + 3$ ☐

$5 + 3 = 10 - 3$ ☐

$7 = 8 - 2$ ☐

Circle the shapes with three sides and cross out (X) the shapes with four corners.

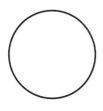   

  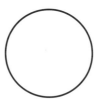 

Join the name to the shape.

| Triangle | Square | Rectangle | Circle |

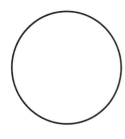  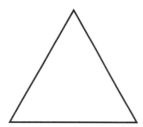 

Draw each of these shapes.

| Rectangle | Square | Circle | Triangle |

Three children put their money together to buy some fruit.

How much do the children have altogether? _____

Natasha buys an orange with 20 p.

How much change will Natasha receive? _____

Pine   Bonsai   Apple   Oak

Which is the tallest tree?   Which is the shortest tree?

....

This is the time now.

Darius will go on holiday in four hours.

Draw the time on the clock when Darius goes on holiday.

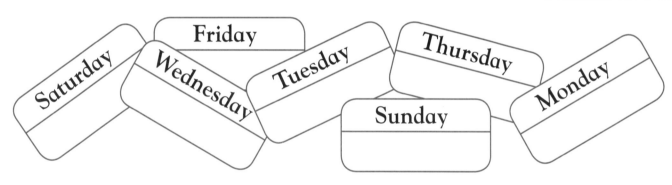

Which are the normal school days?

....

....

Which are the weekend days?

....

Circle the equations that are true.

$4 + 2 = 7$

$6 = 5 + 1$

$4 + 3 = 2 + 5$

Certificate

Ages 5-6

Congratulations to

....

for successfully

finishing this book.

WELL DONE!

You're a star.

Date

....

Answer Section
with Parents' Notes

This book is designed for children who have the ability to count from zero to 20, with a good understanding of the order and value of numbers.

Contents
By working through this book, your child will practise:
- reading, writing, and counting numbers up to 20;
- the concept of same and different;
- the concept of more than and less than;
- the language and symbols of addition;
- the language and symbols of subtraction;
- the concept of simple number bonds;
- continuing simple sequences and patterns;
- recognising simple 2-D shapes;
- classifying and sorting objects into sets;
- describing and comparing sizes and positions.

How to help your child
It is very likely many younger children will not be able to read some of the instructions in this book. Most children can understand maths very well even if they are not yet able to read the language so this should not be a reason to hold them back. Whether children can read or not, there is an expectation that parents or adult helpers will work with children as they progress through this book. Children and their parents/helpers can gain a great deal from working together.

Wherever possible and necessary, try to give your children some practical equipment to help them, especially with the concept of adding and taking away. A collection of counters, buttons, or similar small objects will be invaluable. As they become confident with the activities, the drawn objects may be sufficient.

Build your child's confidence by praise and encouragement. Celebrate their success.

4

★ Read, write, and draw

Write each number as a word.

4 four	8 eight	10 ten	3 three
7 seven	1 one	5 five	9 nine
2 two	6 six	0 zero or nought	

Write each amount as a number and a word.

9
nine

10
ten

7
seven

Draw the correct number of things.

| Four ✩ | Two ☼ | Five ☾ | Three 🚀 |
| ✩ ✩ ✩ ✩ | ☼ ☼ | ☾ ☾ ☾ ☾ ☾ | 🚀 🚀 🚀 |

4

This page provides lots of practice in recognising the number names and correctly forming the numbers themselves. Encourage children to see a correspondence between the number of objects and the number that represents that amount.

5

Tens and units ★

How many in each box?

Tens	Units	Tens	Units	Tens	Units
1	3	2	7	3	9

13   27   39

Draw each number as tens and units.

Tens	Units	Tens	Units	Tens	Units
1	2	2	9	3	6

12   29   36

5

Children will probably use wooden or plastic tens and units equipment at school and should be familiar with them. Recognising that a number such as 15 is composed of one "ten" and five "units" is fundamental.

6

★ Counting

Count in 3s, 4s, 5s, and 6s.

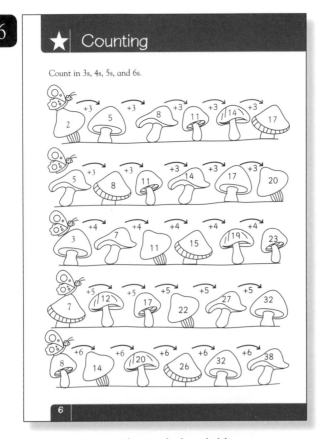

6

Counting in equal steps helps children reinforce the smaller numbers and is, in part, an introduction to times tables.

7

More or less ★

Complete each set.

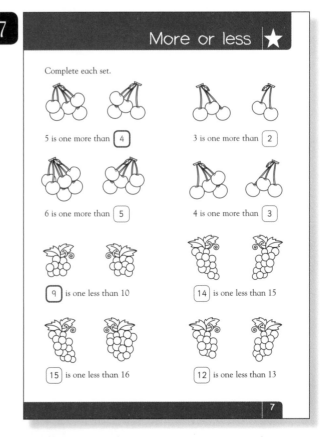

5 is one more than [4]

3 is one more than [2]

6 is one more than [5]

4 is one more than [3]

[9] is one less than 10

[14] is one less than 15

[15] is one less than 16

[12] is one less than 13

7

At this very early stage, it is important for children to learn some of the words that will indicate an operation later on, in this case "more than" representing addition and "less than" representing subtraction.

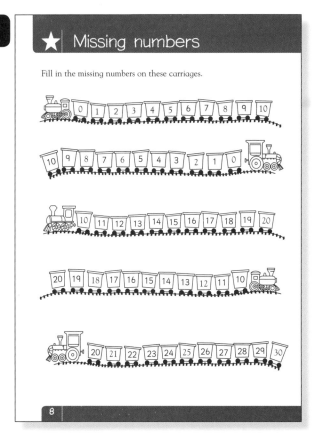

★ Missing numbers

Fill in the missing numbers on these carriages.

This work helps to reinforce the idea of numbers being in an order and to recognise simple sequences.

Counting in 2s ★

Draw the hops and count.

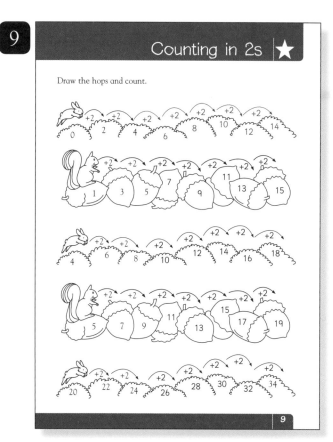

Once again, children will have practice in recognising sequences of the smaller numbers and counting forwards and backwards.

★ Counting in 10s

Fill in the missing numbers.

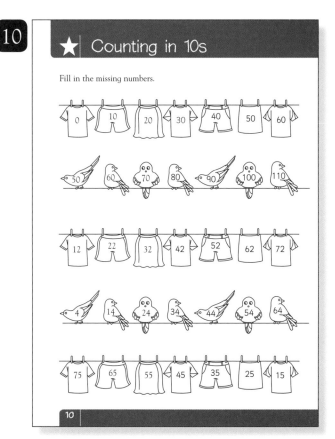

The sequences on this page are a bit more difficult than those before and children may need some support.

Ordering ★

Write the numbers in each cloud in order with the largest number first.

Write the numbers in each cloud in order with the smallest number first.

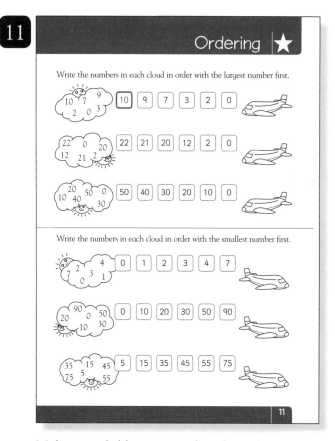

Make sure children notice that the order is sometimes smallest first and sometimes largest first. Reading the question carefully is very important even from this early age!

★ Fractions of shapes

Colour half (½) of each shape.

Now colour half (½) of each shape in a different way.
Answers may vary.

Colour a quarter (¼) of each shape.

Now colour a quarter (¼) of each shape in a different way.
Answers may vary.

What fraction of each shape is shaded?

$\frac{1}{2}$ $\frac{1}{4}$ $\frac{1}{4}$

12

This page invites children to think more imaginatively in the way they divide the shapes. Encourage them to look for the diagonal possibilities and not just the horizontal and vertical lines.

Odd and even ★

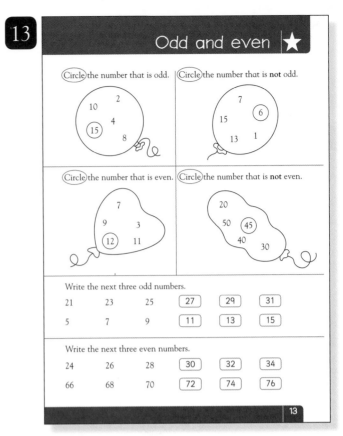

Circle the number that is odd.

Circle the number that is **not** odd.

Circle the number that is even.

Circle the number that is **not** even.

Write the next three odd numbers.

| 21 | 23 | 25 | 27 | 29 | 31 |
| 5 | 7 | 9 | 11 | 13 | 15 |

Write the next three even numbers.

| 24 | 26 | 28 | 30 | 32 | 34 |
| 66 | 68 | 70 | 72 | 74 | 76 |

13

The idea of odd and even numbers is usually picked up quickly by children and will be helpful in later work such as division. You may also wish to explain that even numbers can be equally shared by two whereas odd numbers cannot.

★ Keeping skills sharp

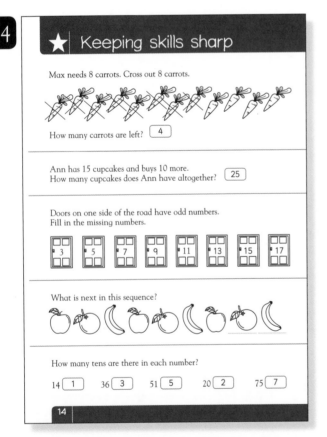

Max needs 8 carrots. Cross out 8 carrots.

How many carrots are left? 4

Ann has 15 cupcakes and buys 10 more.
How many cupcakes does Ann have altogether? 25

Doors on one side of the road have odd numbers.
Fill in the missing numbers.

3 5 7 9 11 13 15 17

What is next in this sequence?

How many tens are there in each number?

14 1   36 3   51 5   20 2   75 7

14

Keeping skills sharp ★

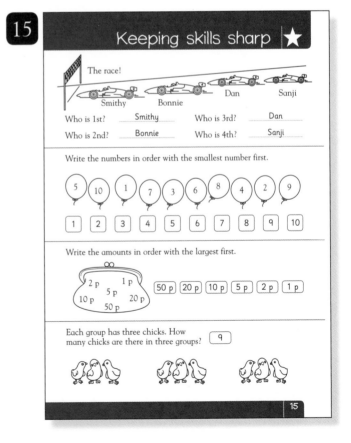

The race!

Smithy   Bonnie   Dan   Sanji

Who is 1st? Smithy   Who is 3rd? Dan
Who is 2nd? Bonnie   Who is 4th? Sanji

Write the numbers in order with the smallest number first.

5 10 1 7 3 6 8 4 2 9

1 2 3 4 5 6 7 8 9 10

Write the amounts in order with the largest first.

2 p 1 p 5 p 20 p 10 p 50 p

50 p 20 p 10 p 5 p 2 p 1 p

Each group has three chicks. How
many chicks are there in three groups? 9

15

The test on this page and the following page should be treated both as a revision and as a chance to see how well your child is learning.

★ Adding up

How many are there in each row?

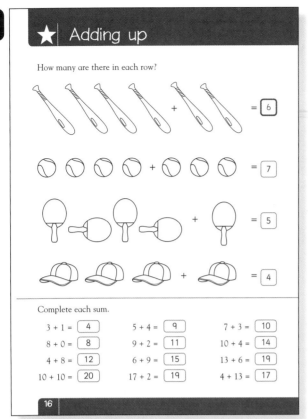

Complete each sum.

3 + 1 = 4   5 + 4 = 9   7 + 3 = 10
8 + 0 = 8   9 + 2 = 11   10 + 4 = 14
4 + 8 = 12   6 + 9 = 15   13 + 6 = 19
10 + 10 = 20   17 + 2 = 19   4 + 13 = 17

Children will have already done addition work at school, but this helps to show how addition is a process of putting groups together. It is important for children to go through the 9 to 10 barrier to understand place values.

Making 10 ★

How many more will make 10?

+ 6 birds

+ 8 birds

+ 9 owls

+ 7 birds

Which number is missing?

3 + 7 = 10   4 + 1 + 5 = 10
9 + 1 = 10   4 + 3 + 3 = 10
5 + 5 = 10   8 + 0 + 2 = 10
4 + 6 = 10   1 + 2 + 7 = 10

Children are encouraged to think about combinations of numbers that add up to 10. The process can be seen as either an addition or subtraction problem, making children see the solution by asking, "How many more do I need?".

★ Subtraction

Reduce each amount by 3. **Hint:** Cross out 3 and count how many are left.

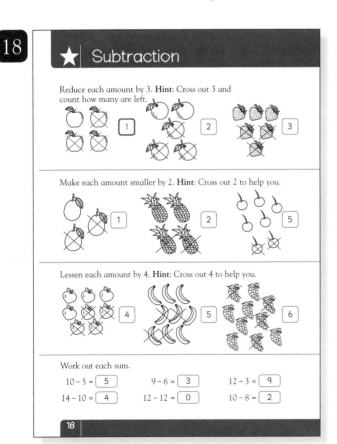

1   2   3

Make each amount smaller by 2. **Hint:** Cross out 2 to help you.

1   2   5

Lessen each amount by 4. **Hint:** Cross out 4 to help you.

4   5   6

Work out each sum.

10 - 5 = 5   9 - 6 = 3   12 - 3 = 9
14 - 10 = 4   12 - 12 = 0   10 - 8 = 2

These simple subtraction problems use terms such as "reduce" and "lessen". The formal subtraction problems are laid out horizontally at this early age.

Taking away ★

How many are left?

Take 2 dots away from each cap.

Take 3 candles away from each cake.

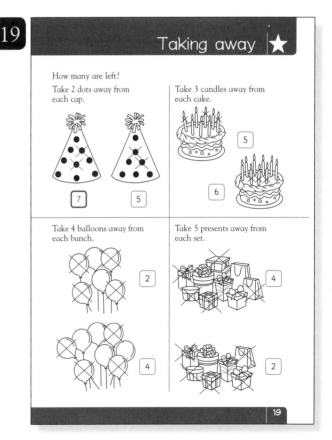

5

7   5

6

Take 4 balloons away from each bunch.

Take 5 presents away from each set.

2   4

4   2

This page combines informal wording with giving children clarity by using everyday objects. Provide children with solid objects such as beads or buttons to help reinforce the concept of subtraction.

★ Doubles

What is double each number?

2 [4]   3 [6]   4 [8]   5 [10]

1 [2]   6 [12]   7 [14]   8 [16]

Double each amount.

5 p [10 p]   2 p [4 p]   10 p [20 p]   20 p [40 p]

1 p [2 p]   4 p [8 p]   6 p [12 p]   11 p [22 p]

What were these numbers before they were doubled?

12 [6]   10 [5]   8 [4]   6 [3]

10 p [5 p]   20 p [10 p]   12 p [6 p]   14 p [7 p]

Try and double these larger numbers.

30 [60]   40 [80]   50 [100]   100 [200]

15 p [30 p]   25 p [50 p]   60 p [£1.20]   £6.00 [£12]

"Double" and "doubling" are typical of the variety of mathematical vocabulary children will encounter over the years. You may also want to explain that doubling whole numbers always produces even numbers.

Counting in groups ★

Count in groups and write how many there are.

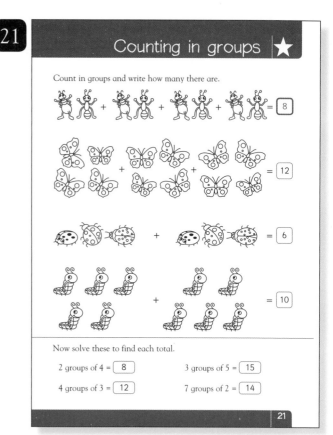

Now solve these to find each total.

2 groups of 4 = [8]   3 groups of 5 = [15]

4 groups of 3 = [12]   7 groups of 2 = [14]

The use of "groups of" is a common way to introduce multiplication and times tables although children need to know that these things are the same as repeated addition, just a lot quicker!

★ Keeping skills sharp

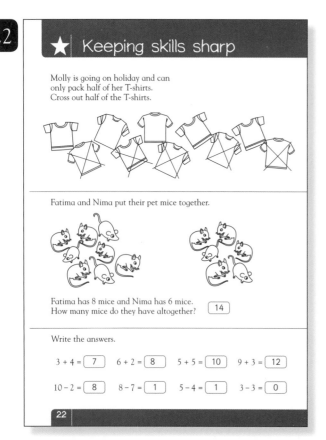

Molly is going on holiday and can only pack half of her T-shirts. Cross out half of the T-shirts.

Fatima and Nima put their pet mice together.

Fatima has 8 mice and Nima has 6 mice. How many mice do they have altogether? [14]

Write the answers.

3 + 4 = [7]   6 + 2 = [8]   5 + 5 = [10]   9 + 3 = [12]

10 − 2 = [8]   8 − 7 = [1]   5 − 4 = [1]   3 − 3 = [0]

As with the previous test, this one reviews some of the topics already covered. Sometimes, your child has to work out what is the best operation to use to solve the problem.

Keeping skills sharp ★

Fill in the box with the right symbol: <, >, or = .

32 [>] 12   15 [=] 15   17 [<] 21

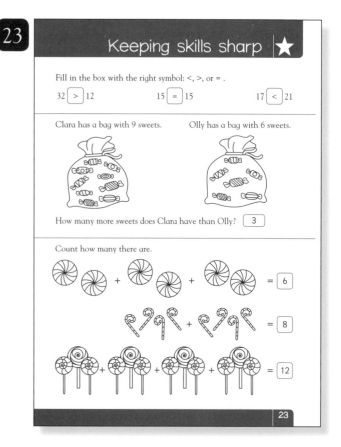

Clara has a bag with 9 sweets.   Olly has a bag with 6 sweets.

How many more sweets does Clara have than Olly? [3]

Count how many there are.

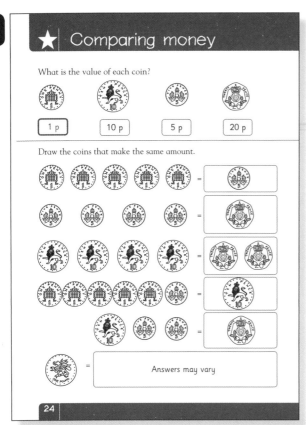

Comparing money

What is the value of each coin?

| 1 p | 10 p | 5 p | 20 p |

Draw the coins that make the same amount.

Answers may vary

This work quickly progresses from helping children recognise the coins to working out what combinations make other amounts, e.g. five 1 pence coins are equivalent to one 5 pence coin. The more practical help the better.

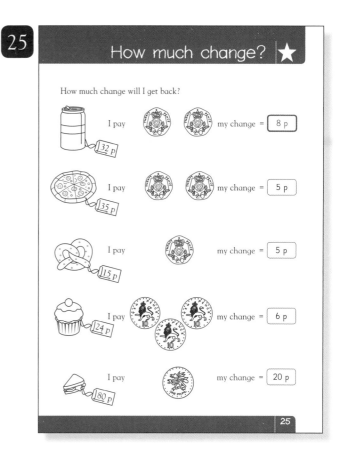

How much change?

How much change will I get back?

I pay ... my change = 8 p
32 p

I pay ... my change = 5 p
35 p

I pay ... my change = 5 p
15 p

I pay ... my change = 6 p
24 p

I pay ... my change = 20 p
80 p

Realising or working out what change is needed is a very useful skill for children and the more practical help the better. Giving them some pocket money and then going with them to the shops to spend some of it would be useful.

Comparing sizes

Circle the largest animal in each group.

Circle the smallest animal in each group.

Circle the animal that is the tallest.

Circle the caterpillar that is the longest.

To an adult, these problems and words can seem very simplistic but it is surprising how often children become confused. To be sure they really are getting the hang of it, throw them a few extra "homemade" questions as and when appropriate.

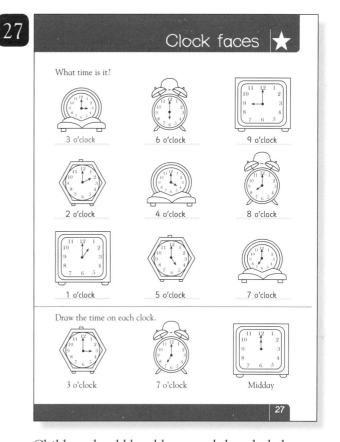

Clock faces

What time is it?

3 o'clock   6 o'clock   9 o'clock

2 o'clock   4 o'clock   8 o'clock

1 o'clock   5 o'clock   7 o'clock

Draw the time on each clock.

3 o'clock   7 o'clock   Midday

Children should be able to read the whole hours fairly well by now and draw them on blank clock faces. Many children are more used to digital displays and not so confident with analogue faces that can vary widely.

⭐ | Equal or not

Which equations are true and which are false?
Mark each of them with a T for True or an F for False.

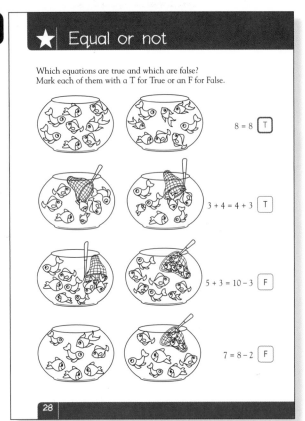

8 = 8 [T]

3 + 4 = 4 + 3 [T]

5 + 3 = 10 − 3 [F]

7 = 8 − 2 [F]

This page reinforces the meaning of an equal sign in equations. Here children are given practice on understanding that each side of an equation must have the same value in order to be equal.

2-D shapes | ⭐

Circle the shapes with three sides and cross out (X) the shapes with four corners.

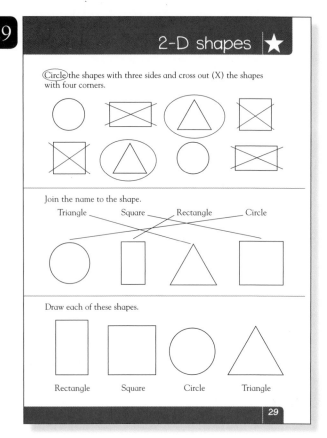

Join the name to the shape.

Triangle   Square   Rectangle   Circle

Draw each of these shapes.

Rectangle   Square   Circle   Triangle

Children will probably know the names of most simple shapes but may not be aware of attributes such as "side", "surface", or "corner".

⭐ | Keeping skills sharp

Three children put their money together to buy some fruit.

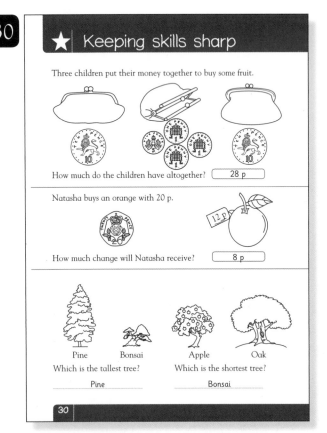

How much do the children have altogether? [28 p]

Natasha buys an orange with 20 p.

How much change will Natasha receive? [8 p]

Pine   Bonsai   Apple   Oak

Which is the tallest tree?   Which is the shortest tree?

Pine   Bonsai

This is the final test that covers much of the ground from the final third of the book. The test can be given a few times with a break in between and comparisons made between the results.

Keeping skills sharp | ⭐

This is the time now.   Darius will go on holiday in four hours.

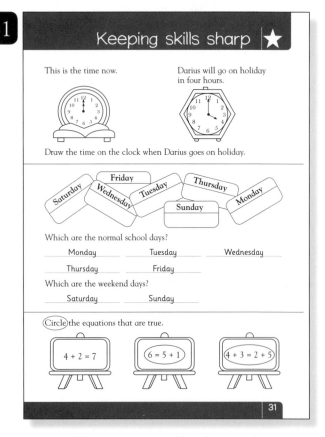

Draw the time on the clock when Darius goes on holiday.

Saturday   Friday   Wednesday   Tuesday   Thursday   Sunday   Monday

Which are the normal school days?

Monday   Tuesday   Wednesday

Thursday   Friday

Which are the weekend days?

Saturday   Sunday

Circle the equations that are true.

4 + 2 = 7   6 = 5 + 1   4 + 3 = 2 + 5

The *Maths Made Easy* workbooks provide more practice pages.